Follow the li...

Trace over the lines from each princess to h...

Princess
Amber

wand

Princess
Ruby

ring

Princess
Alice

comb

Princess
Tabitha

slippers

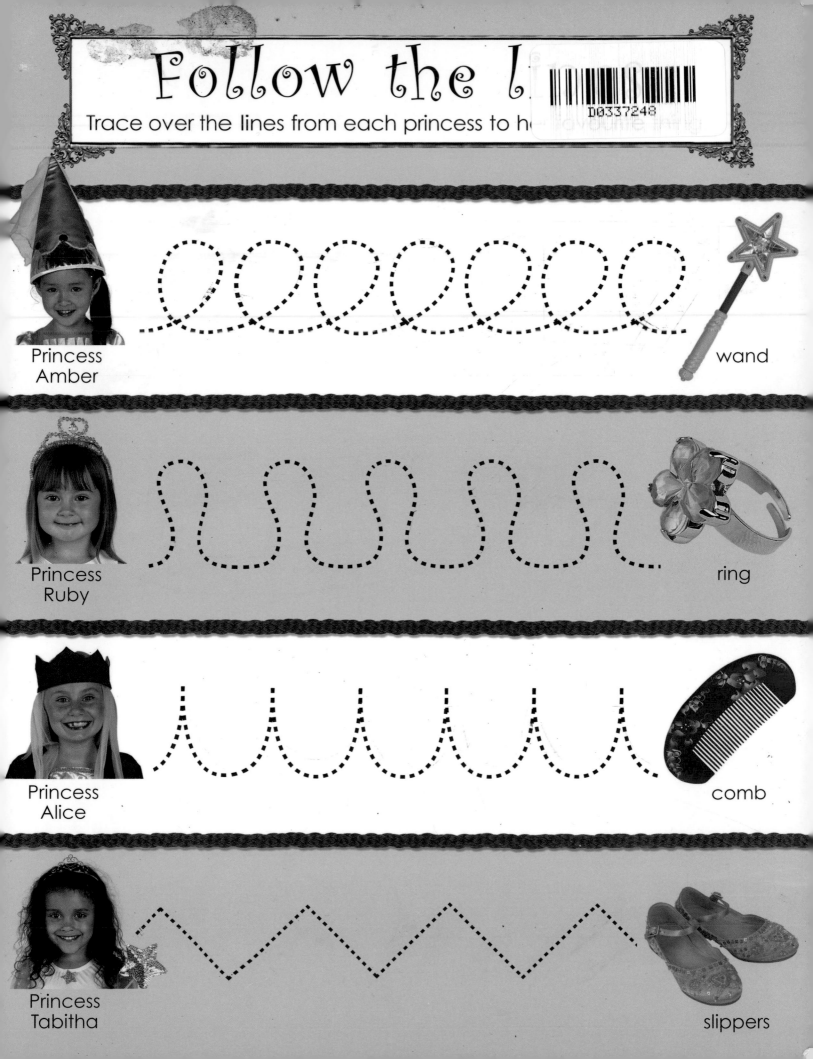

Connect the dots

Connect the dots to complete the pictures,
then trace over the word.

wand

crown

Princess path

Which path will lead the princess to Prince Charming?

Princess Tabitha

A   B   C

frog

pumpkin

Prince Charming

Missing letters

Fill in the missing letters to complete the princess words.

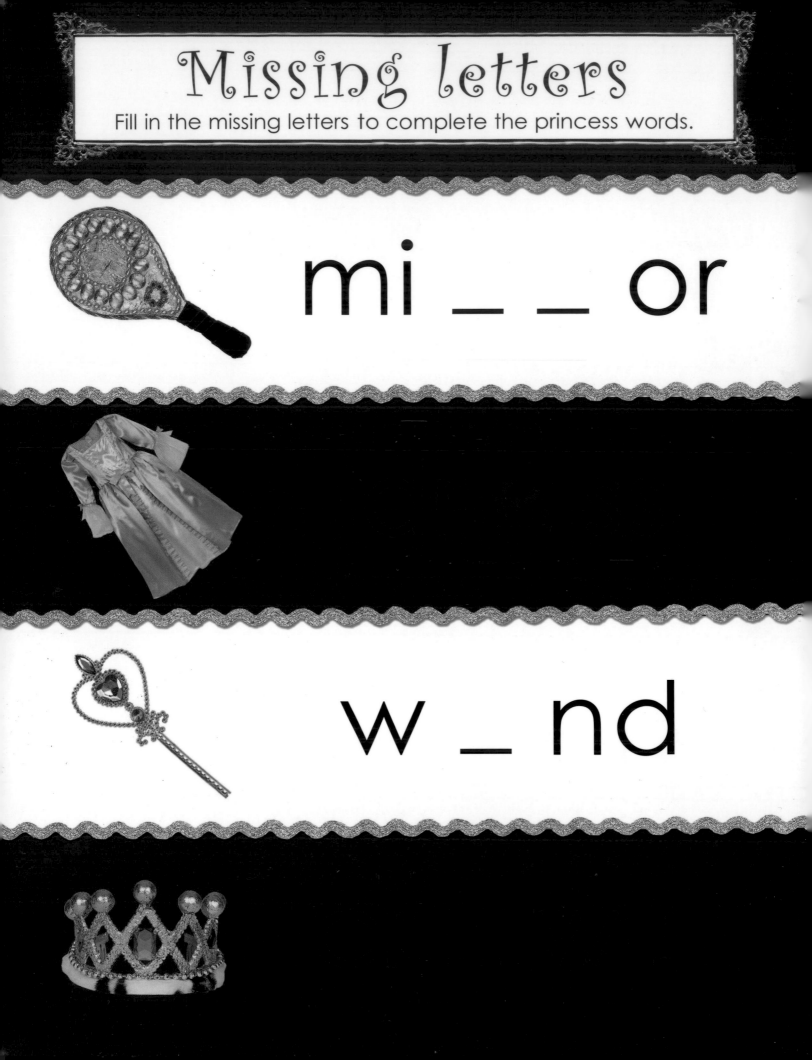

mi _ _ or

w _ nd

Prince portrait

Trace over the outlines to draw the picture and write the word.

prince

prince

Counting Jewels

Count each row of jewels and write the numbers in the boxes.

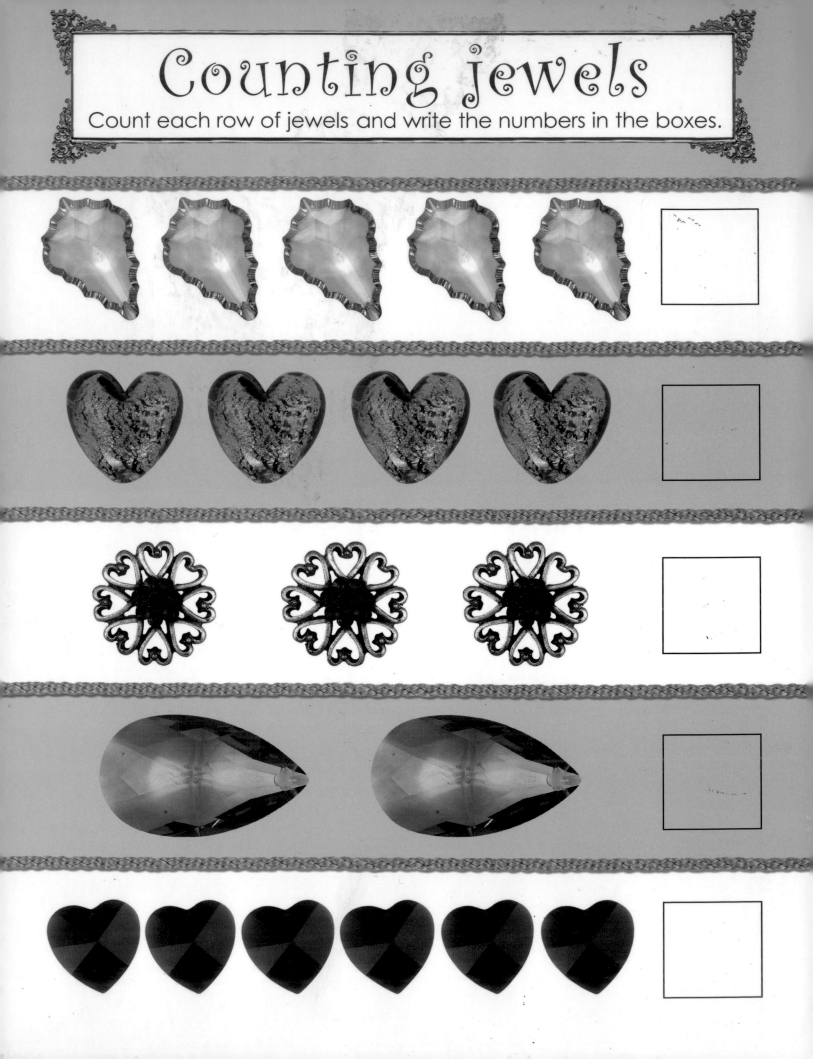

Trace and draw

Look at the picture and the word, then trace over the outlines.

hat

look

hat

trace

Now draw the hat and write the word.

h___

What's different?

There are six differences between these two pictures.
Circle each difference on picture B when you find them.

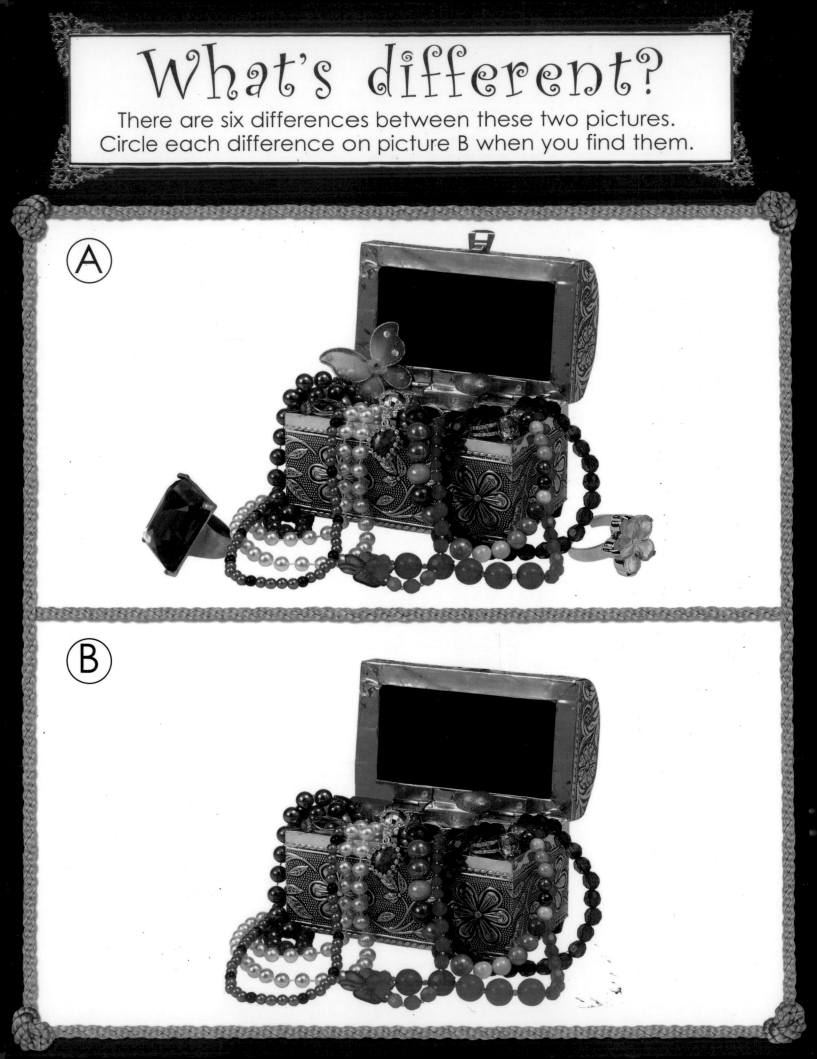

Princess maze

Guide the princess along the enchanted
path to find her white horse.

Start

Finish

Princess counting

Count the princess things and write the numbers of each in the boxes.

How many pairs of slippers can you count?

How many dresses can you count?

How many
tiaras
can you
count?

How many
white horses
can you
count?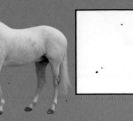

How many
mirrors
can you
count?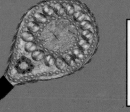

How many
rings
can you
count?

Mix and match

Draw a line to link each princess to her favourite thing.

Princess Tabitha

Princess Amber

Princess Jessica

Princess Alice

crown

mirror

perfume

brush